A Falcon *littlehawk* book

Jesus at work

Stories and Prayers for children by Beryl Bye
Illustrated by Joyce Badrocke

First published December 1969
Reprinted May 1971
Copyright Beryl J. Bye 1969
Illustrations and cover Joyce Badrocke, Des. RCA
SBN 85491 522 2

Overseas agents
CSSM and Crusader Bookroom Society Ltd,
177 Manchester Street, Christchurch,
New Zealand

Sunday School Centre Wholesale, P.O. Box 3020,
Cape Town, South Africa

EMU Book Agencies Ltd, 511 Kent Street,
Sydney, N.S.W., Australia

Published for the Church Pastoral Aid Society,
Falcon Court, 32 Fleet Street, London EC4Y 1DB

Printed in Great Britain by
Albert Gait Ltd, Grimsby, England

Contents

For parents   5

1 The Mummy who had some good news   6
   St Luke 1. 27-38

2 The Baby who was born in a shed   10
   St Luke 2. 1-20

3 The Boy who forgot the time   15
   St Luke 2. 41-52

4 The Friends who made a hole in the roof 20
   St Luke 5. 18-26

5 The Fishermen who got caught in a
   storm   25
   St Matthew 8. 23-27

6 The Man who climbed up a tree   31
   St Luke 19. 1-10

7 The Donkey that had never been ridden   36
   St Mark 11. 1-11

8 The Rich Man who didn't want to give
   anything away   41
   St Mark 10. 17-22

9 The Temple that was used as a market   46
   St John 2. 13-16

10 The Boy who shared his lunch   50
   St John 6. 1-14

11 The Widow who had nothing left   55
   St Mark 12. 41-44

12 The Sick Man who remembered to say
   thank you   59
   St Luke 17. 11-19

For
Andrew and Claire
and Alison Jane

For parents

"Jesus at Work" the fourth in the Littlehawk Series covers the Nativity Story, a few of the miracles, and some of the occasions when Jesus met and talked with individuals.

Once more I have tried to tell the stories in a way that will make them relevant to a small child's way of life and line of thought.

As Littlehawk Books are sold separately, and not as a set, it is necessary to repeat in the "parents page" of each book the reminder that the books are intended to be "shared *with*" and not "handed *to*" your small son or daughter.

Right from the opening sentence of the first story it will be obvious that pictures and stories are closely linked, so that the child absorbs the story both visually and verbally. Parents should take full advantage of any free discussion that this picture-story method may open out.

Finally, may I share with you a six year old's comment on a previous book in this series. It made me feel that, perhaps, I had not been too unsuccessful in my aim to immerse myself in a child's world whilst writing these stories.

"Mummy!" he said, "How does Auntie Beryl KNOW all the things we think and do?"!

BERYL BYE

1 The mummy who had some good news

Do you like this picture of a big dog looking after a baby deer? The dog is the little deer's foster-father. That means that he looks after and takes care of the little deer just as if he was the deer's real father. This really happened in a Wildlife Park in Norfolk.

I am going to tell you a story about a Mummy and a little baby boy, and a kind foster-father who helped the Mummy look after him, just as if he was the baby's real father.

Have you ever heard of a town crier? There is a picture of one on the other page. A town crier's job was to tell all the news in the days before we had newspapers and radios and television sets.

There is an angel beside the town crier. God

sometimes used to send angels to people to tell them any special news that He wanted them to know.

One day, nearly 2,000 years ago, an angel brought some good news to a girl called Mary. Mary was engaged to be married to a man called Joseph.

"Mary" the angel said, "I have come to tell you that very soon you are going to have a little baby boy."

Mary was very surprised.

"But I'm not even married yet" she said, "I'm only engaged." (Mummies and Daddies don't usually have babies until after they are married.)

"I know that" the angel said, "But this is going to be a very special baby. Joseph is not going to be the baby's real father, he's going to be his 'foster-father' because you see the baby's real father is going to be God Himself."

"He's going to have quite a lot of names" the angel went on, "One of His names will be Jesus, and another will be 'The Son of the Most High'. That's to remind people who His Father really is."

Mary was very pleased and excited.

"If God thinks He can trust me to be the Mummy of His little son, I think I'm very, very lucky." she said. And she sang a little song just to show how happy she was.

When the angel had gone, Mary was just longing to tell someone her good news. Do you always want to tell someone when something nice or exciting happens to you?

"I'll go and tell my cousin Elizabeth" she said. "She's going to have a baby too, so I know she will be pleased to know my news."

And Elizabeth WAS pleased! She listened to everything Mary had to say and then gave her a big hug. You can see her in the picture.

"It was nice of you to come and tell me" she said, "I'm sure your baby is going to be Someone very Special, and you are very special too because you are going to be His Mummy."

I'm glad Elizabeth was so pleased about Mary's good news, aren't you?

Are you pleased when your friend or your cousin tells you about something nice that has happened to them, or are you a bit sulky and jealous and wish it was you?

I think Joseph and Elizabeth were both very kind people, don't you? Joseph, because he was going to look after God's little Son just as if He was his own baby, and Elizabeth because she was so happy and glad about Mary's good news.

A Prayer:
Dear God, Please help me to be really happy and pleased when nice or exciting things happen to other people, so that my friends always want to share their good news with me; and help me to be kind to little babies and small animals, so that they learn to love and trust me. Amen.

2 The baby who was born in a shed

Do you like Christmas? I expect you do! Most boys and girls have lots of lovely presents at Christmas, and they like to give presents as well. The children in the picture are wrapping up presents for their Mummy and Daddy! Do you know why people give presents to each other at Christmas? I think I'll tell you about it.

Joseph—that was the name of the man who was to be Mary's baby's foster father—was rather worried. He had to go on a long journey and he wanted to take Mary with him.

"It's nearly time for your baby to be born" he

said, "I hope he won't be born while we are away from home."

"I don't expect he will" Mary said, "I don't think he is quite ready to be born yet."

But do you know, Mary was quite wrong! No sooner had Mary and Joseph arrived at Bethlehem, which was the name of the village they were visiting, than Mary knew that it was time for her baby to be born.

"We must find somewhere to stay!" Joseph said, but everywhere was full! So many people were staying in Bethlehem that night that there wasn't one spare bed. There wasn't even room for Mary and Joseph to spread their blankets on the floor!

Poor Mary was very tired, and Joseph didn't know what to do, when at last they met a very kind man.

"My house is quite full up" he said, "But there is a shed beside the house. It is full of clean straw and hay, and I keep my animals there, but I can move them into one corner so that there will be room for you as well." (You can see him telling Mary and Joseph about it, in the picture.)

Mary and Joseph were very grateful.

"Thank you very much" they said, and they followed the man into the shed and made themselves comfy on the soft dry hay.

Not long after that the little baby Jesus was born. Mary hadn't got a cradle or a carry-cot for Him, so she rolled Him up in a long strip of woollen material and laid Him gently in the stone manger where the food for the cows and donkeys was usually put. (You can see the manger in the picture.)

It wasn't long before visitors started to arrive. New-born babies usually have lots of visitors, don't they?

First it was some shepherds.

"We were looking after our sheep on the hillside when an angel came and told us about your special baby," they said. "And we came all the way down to the village to find Him."

Mary and Joseph were very pleased to show the baby Jesus to the shepherds.

"Thank you for coming" they said, when the shepherds went away again.

Some time after that, Jesus had some more visitors. These visitors were very important and they brought the baby some very expensive presents. One of them brought Him some real gold! Another visitor brought Him a bottle of special scent called Frankincense that was used specially to make churches smell nice. A third visitor brought Him a kind of medicine called myrrh that helped to make you better if you had a bad pain. (You can see the presents in the picture.)

They were rather special presents, weren't they?

They weren't the ordinary kind of presents that you take to give a little baby. But then the baby Jesus wasn't an ordinary kind of baby, was He?

So you see, that is why we give gifts to each other at Christmas. It is to remind us about the baby Jesus who was born in a shed, and the three important visitors who came to bring Him presents.

A Prayer:
Dear Father God, Please bless all new little babies and their Mummies and Daddies. Help me to think about the baby Jesus when I give and receive presents at Christmas-time. Amen.

3 The boy who forgot the time

Do you sometimes forget the time? Perhaps Mummy comes and tells you it's time to get ready to go shopping, but you're so interested in playing in the sandpit that you forget all about what she has said! This is what happened to the boy in the picture!

When Jesus was a boy, He forgot the time and I'm going to tell you how it happened.

Every year Mary and Joseph—that was Jesus' real Mummy and His foster father—went up to the big town of Jerusalem for a special kind of Church service. It was called the Passover Festival and it was held in the Temple, which was a very big and important church.

The village where Jesus lived was called Nazareth, and it was quite a long way from Jerusalem, so all the people who were going up to the Passover Festival decided to go together in a big party. It was great fun!

Jesus was very excited when He knew He was going to the Passover Festival, and I expect He longed and longed for the day to come, just like you do when Mummy and Daddy have arranged a special outing.

When the service was over and everyone gathered together ready to go home again, Mary and Joseph couldn't find Jesus. There were so many people, and the boys and girls were all dashing around so quickly (like boys and girls always do) that they just couldn't seem to pick Jesus out.

"I'm sure He's here somewhere" Joseph said, "It's just that all the boys and girls look alike, and there's so many of them. He knew where we were meeting and what time we were leaving. We'll soon find Him once we start on the way back."

Mary wasn't so sure, but she didn't say anything. She just kept looking round anxiously as they started home, and kept hoping that Jesus would soon appear.

But do you know, Jesus wasn't there at all!

He had stayed behind in the Temple and had found some very interesting people to talk to. They were teachers who knew a lot about God and Jesus enjoyed talking to them so much that He forgot all about the time. (You can see Him in the picture.)

Mary and Joseph and the rest of the party had travelled a whole day's journey away from Jerusalem, and then Mary refused to go any further.

"I'm sure Jesus is not with us" she said, "We must go back and look for Him."

I don't expect Joseph was very pleased, do you? (You can see them going back for Jesus in the picture.)

They looked absolutely everywhere, and at last they found Him. He was in the Temple, sitting on the floor listening to some of the clever teachers and asking them questions as well!

Mary was really quite cross!

"Why have you treated us like this? " she said to Jesus, "Your father and I have been very worried. We've been looking for you everywhere."

Jesus was very surprised. You see, He had quite forgotten the time!

"Why were you looking for me?" He said, "Didn't you know that I would be in my Father's House?" (And He meant His Real Father's House, didn't He?)

"Well, you must come home with us at once," Mary said, "We've wasted enough time already."

I think Mary knew that Jesus didn't really mean to be naughty and she understood that finding out all that you can about God is very, very important. And I'm sure Jesus realized that Mary was only cross because she was worried about not finding Him, because Mummies DO get cross when they're worried, don't they?

LOST!
Boy,
12 years
old.
Last seen in
Jerusalem

A Prayer:
Dear Lord Jesus, I know You understand when I sometimes forget the time because I'm doing things that are very interesting. Help Mummy and Daddy to understand why I forget and help me to understand why they get cross. Amen.

4 The friends who made a hole in the roof

Are you a 'keep trying' or a 'give up easily' kind of girl or boy? Do you say "I can't do that", or do you sit down and think really hard about a way to do it?

This is a story about four friends who were 'keep on trying' kind of people, and they always said "There must be a way . . . " instead of "We can't do that!"

I have told you two stories about when Jesus was a baby, and one story about when He was a little boy. Now I'm going to tell you some stories about some of the wonderful things that He did when He was a young man.

You will remember that Jesus was a really special kind of person, because God was His 'Daddy', and so of course He could do some really special things.

One of the 'special things' was to make people quite well just by touching them—even if they had been ill for a very long time.

One day the four 'keep on trying' friends heard about Jesus.

"I wish He could come here" they said to each other. "We could ask Him to come and visit our friend who is ill, and He would lay His hands upon him, and he would be quite well again."

"He's been ill for such a long time" another of the friends said sadly. "He can't even walk now, but has to stay in bed all the time. I don't see how we can get him to Jesus, even though He isn't far away."

Now you will remember that these four friends were not 'give up easily' kind of people, and so they sat down and had a really good think.

"I know how we could take him to Jesus" one of them said suddenly, when he had been thinking for a very long time. "We could carry him. There are four of us, and four corners to his bed. If we each took one corner, we could carry him between us quite easily."

And that is just what they did. They picked up the blankets on which their friend was lying, and carried him between them all the way to Jesus! (You can see them in the picture.)

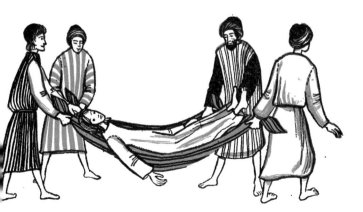

When they got to the house where Jesus was staying, there were lots and lots of people there. There were so many people, that you couldn't see the door of the house at all, and you certainly couldn't get anywhere near it.

"We mustn't give up!" one of the friends said, "We must think of another way of getting inside."

They thought, and they thought, and they thought, and then suddenly they had an idea! There was a little stone staircase running up the outside of the house, and once they were on the roof, they knew exactly what they would do.

I expect the sick man felt a bit 'wobbly' being carried up the staircase don't you? I wonder if he was afraid that he might fall? But the friends were very, very careful, and at last they were all safely on the flat roof of the house. (You can see them in the picture.)

Then the friends knelt down on the roof and carefully started to take away the tiles until at last they had made a big hole! I don't expect the man who owned the house was very pleased, but I'm sure the friends were careful to see that the tiles didn't get broken, so that they could put them back afterwards. They could see Jesus standing inside the house talking to the people, so they fastened long ropes to the corners of the blankets, and lowered their sick friend gently down until he lay right in front of Jesus. Jesus was surprised! He looked up and saw the four friends gathered round the outside of the hole looking down.

"What a lot of trouble you have taken to bring

23

your friend to Me" He said, "I will certainly make him quite well again."

"Get up, pick up your blankets and go home" He said to the sick man, "You are quite well now."

At once the man sprang to his feet, picked up the bedding on which he used to lie, and went off home.

I DO hope he remembered to thank his four clever friends, don't you?

A Prayer:
Dear God, Please help me to be a 'keep on trying' kind of person, so that I don't give up easily when things are hard to do. Amen.

5 The fishermen who got caught in a storm

When you go to the seaside does Daddy sometimes take you out in a boat? I expect he makes sure that it is a nice calm day and even then makes you wear a life-jacket so that you would be quite safe if you fell into the water. (The little boy in the picture is wearing a life-jacket.)

One day Jesus and His friends went out in a boat. It was a nice calm day and Jesus was very

tired, so His friends made Him comfy with a cushion and told Him to settle down for a little nap. The boat bobbed gently up and down on the little blue waves and in no time at all Jesus was fast asleep.

Not long after that the sun went in. The sky became all dark and cloudy and a nasty cold wind started to blow.

"There's going to be a storm" one of Jesus' friends said. "The waves have all gone grey and choppy and some of them are washing right into the boat."

"I'm frightened!" another friend said. "I wish Jesus would wake up and DO something instead of lying there fast alseep as if nothing was the matter."

"Let's wake Him up!" someone else said. "If we don't do something quickly we shall all be drowned!"

By this time the storm was really dreadful! The sun had disappeared altogether and the lightning was making a jiggly-jaggly pattern right across the sky. The thunder was banging too— like someone jumping about noisily in the bedroom when Mummy is springcleaning and there isn't any carpet on the floor.

The friends really felt quite cross that Jesus was still asleep when they were wide awake and so terribly frightened.

"Lord, save us!" they shouted at Him, "We are drowning" which was a bit of a fib really, because they couldn't really say they were DROWNING when they were still safely in the boat! You can see them waking Jesus up in the picture.

Jesus sat up and rubbed His eyes.

"What are you so frightened about?" He said in surprise.

The friends thought that was a very silly question when there was such a dreadful storm and everyone was getting very wet! Jesus just stood there and looked at the storm. He wasn't afraid! He thought it was all rather wonderful and exciting.

"Quieten down" He said to the wind. "You are frightening my friends" and suddenly the wind went very quiet.

"Don't be so rough" He said to the waves, "You are making the boat heave about" and the waves became quiet again.

"Don't be so noisy" He said to the thunder, "You are waking people up" and the thunder stopped banging about.

"Don't darken the sky" He said to the clouds, "You are making it seem like the middle of the night" and the clouds parted, so that the sun could shine right through again.

"Isn't He wonderful?" Jesus' friends said. "Even the wind and the waves do just what He tells them to. We must always remember that we never need be frightened when Jesus is here to make sure that everything is all right."

I hope after that they let Jesus go back to sleep again, don't you?

A Prayer:
Dear Lord Jesus, I know that I need never be frightened because You are always with me, to look after me, and to make sure that nothing can hurt me. Remind me about this if I feel a bit worried next time there is a big storm. Amen.

6 The man who climbed up a tree

Do you sometimes get 'fed up' because you are not very tall? Perhaps you are too small to look over the top of shop counters, or see all that is happening when there is a Punch and Judy Show on the beach.

This story is about a man who wasn't very tall and his name was Zaccheus.

Zaccheus lived in Jericho and he was a very rich man, but I am sorry to tell you that he wasn't a very honest one. He worked for the Roman Government and his job was to collect money from the people to pay the soldiers in the Roman Army, and to build roads and bridges. The people were very cross about having to give money to

the Roman Government, and they were even crosser when Zaccheus used to collect more money than he ought to have done, because he always added on a little bit for himself. Can you see him doing this in the picture? Nobody liked Zaccheus, so although he lived in a very nice house with a very big garden, and had lots of servants, he didn't have any friends at all.

One day Zaccheus heard that Someone Special had come to the town of Jericho. It was Jesus. Zaccheus had heard a lot about Jesus and he very much wanted to meet Him.

"I'll go out into the road" he said to himself, "and have a good look at Him when He goes by."

But when Zaccheus got outside he found that there were hundreds and hundreds of people. They ALL wanted to see Jesus and poor Zaccheus couldn't find a spare peep-hole anywhere.

"I hate being so short!" Zaccheus said to himself. "If only I was taller I could see right over the heads of all the people and have a really good view."

He pushed and he shoved and he jostled and he elbowed his way into the crowd, but no one was going to give up their place to the cross little tax-collector whom no one liked.

Then Zaccheus looked up and saw a tree. It was growing just at the side of the roadway and its branches hung right over the road, making a nice big shady patch. Zaccheus hadn't climbed a tree since he was quite a little boy, but he made up his mind to climb one now! Looking round to make sure that no one was looking he tucked

his long striped robe up
round his waist
and scrambled up
into its branches.
(Can you see him
in the picture?)

He could see beautifully! But no one could see him! Zaccheus was VERY pleased with himself.

Jesus was coming down the road. Now He was nearly there! Now He was there! Suddenly He stopped—right underneath the tree where Zaccheus was hiding. Then He looked up.

"Zaccheus" He called, "Hurry up and come down from that tree. I want to come to tea with you today."

Zaccheus was surprised. How had Jesus known that he was in the tree? How had Jesus known his name? Why did Jesus want to be HIS guest—the cross little tax-collector whom everyone hated? He climbed down from the tree very quickly and hurried to make Jesus welcome in his house.

All the other people were very cross.

"Why does Jesus want to stay with HIM?" they muttered, "He's one of the nastiest, and wickedest, and crossest men in the town."

But do you know after Jesus had stayed with him Zaccheus became quite a different kind of person! He paid everybody back four times as much money as he had taken and gave away half of all the money he had saved to the poor. Everyone was very surprised. Soon Zaccheus had lots and lots of friends, and was so happy and jolly that you wouldn't have known that he was the same man. Of course he still wasn't very tall, but that didn't worry him any more because when you're little AND NICE, people always manage to squeeze you in at the front of the crowd, or find you something to stand on so that you can see better.

A Prayer:

Dear Lord Jesus, Please help me to be honest about things like taking sweets that don't belong to me, or giving Mummy the right change when I have been to the shops. Remind me not to push and shove but to ask nicely when I'm not tall enough to see. Amen.

7 The donkey that had never been ridden

The boy and girl in the picture are riding donkeys on the sands. Do you ride a donkey when you go to the seaside? Long ago, at the time when Jesus lived on earth, most people rode donkeys when they wanted to go on a long journey. Some of the very rich people rode horses or camels, but ordinary people like you and me, rode donkeys because they didn't cost so much to buy, and didn't eat so much food.

One day, Jesus wanted to go on quite a long journey. He needed a donkey, but He hadn't a donkey of His own, because He always gave all His money away and didn't keep any for Himself. While He was still wondering what to do He met a friend.

"Good morning," the friend said, "How are you?"

"I'm very well, thank you" Jesus said, "But I'm just wondering what to do. I want to go to Jerusalem and I really need a donkey to ride, and I haven't got a donkey of my own."

"Oh, that's all right!" the friend said at once. "I've a colt" (that's the name for a young donkey or pony). "He's very young and rather frisky" (frisky means 'jumping all over the place and bouncing about'!) "But you are very welcome to borrow him, if you like."

"Thank you very much" Jesus said. "I'll send some of my friends to fetch him tomorrow. I'll take great care of him and let you have him back safely afterwards."

"I'll tell my servants that I've given you permission to borrow my colt" the friend said, "Then if I'm out when they come, they can just take him away."

The next morning Jesus asked his friends to go and collect the donkey.

"If anyone tries to stop you taking him, just say 'The Lord needs it and will send it back afterwards' " He said. "My friend said it will be quite all right."

When Jesus' friends arrived at the farm they found the colt tied up by a doorway. They went

up and started to untie him. You can see them in the picture.

"Hey! What do you think you're doing?" some men who were standing there shouted, "Who said you could untie the colt?"

"The Lord needs it and will send it back afterwards" Jesus' friends said, just as He had told them.

"Oh, that's all right" the men said, "We remember the Master said he was lending the donkey to a friend of his, who wanted to make a journey to Jerusalem."

The donkey was VERY frisky! He jumped about all over the place, and kept pretending he could see things in the hedge which frightened him AWFULLY! Then he pretended he could hear something VERY dangerous coming up behind him, and he tried to gallop away! Jesus' friends got rather cross with him, and were very hot and tired by the time they had got him home again.

"You'll never be able to ride him!" they told Jesus. "I don't think anyone has ridden him before, and he's VERY frisky!"

But do you know, as soon as Jesus took hold of the donkey's halter, the donkey became quite quiet. (A halter is a piece of rope that is knotted round a donkey's nose and ears so that you can guide him.)

Jesus stroked the donkey's nose, and then laid His cloak across the donkey's back for a kind of saddle, and the donkey didn't mind at all! Then Jesus climbed on his back, and the donkey didn't mind that either! Then Jesus made a clicking noise to the donkey to show him that it was time to go. (Daddy will show you how to make the clicking noise if you ask him!)

"I wonder why he was so naughty with US" Jesus' friends must have said to each other.

So Jesus rode all the way to Jerusalem on the borrowed donkey, and he was as good as gold! Even when people cheered because they were pleased to see Jesus, he was as good as gold; even when they spread their coats in the road, waved branches of the palm trees in the air and called "Hurrah for Jesus!" the donkey didn't mind a bit! (You can see this happening in the picture.)

I'm glad that man lent his little donkey to Jesus, and I'm glad the donkey behaved so beautifully, aren't you? Do you sometimes lend things to people you know? I hope you do.

A Prayer:
Dear Lord Jesus, Help me to enjoy working for You as much as the little donkey did, and make me willing to lend my tricycle or doll's pram to my friends who haven't one of their own. Amen.

8 The rich man who didn't want to give anything away

Have you got a favourite toy, or doll, or book that you like better than anything else? Perhaps, when you have friends to play, you don't mind them playing with any of the rest of your toys, but you put your favourite thing away, safely, because you don't really want to share it! (That's what the girl in the picture is doing!)

Jesus once talked to a man who was like that. The man came running up to Him, just as Jesus had started off upon a journey, and throwing himself on the ground in front of Jesus, he asked Him a question.

"Good Master" he said, "What must I do if I want to be sure of going to heaven?"

"Well," said Jesus, "What about the 'rules for being good' that Moses gave you? Do you remember them and try to keep them?" (Moses was a very wise teacher who loved God very much and who lived a long, long time before Jesus was born.)

"Yes" said the man, "I'm very good at remembering and keeping the rules. I have never killed anyone. I have never stolen anyone else's wife, I haven't taken anything that doesn't belong to me. I don't tell lies, I don't cheat, and I'm polite to my father and mother and always do as they say."

(He sounds as if he was a VERY good young man doesn't he? I wouldn't like to say I have always been as good as that, would you?)

Jesus looked straight at the young man—He gazed right into his eyes, the way that Mummy and Daddy do when they want to be sure you are telling the truth.

"Yes" Jesus said to Himself. "He really is a very nice young man and I do believe he is telling the truth."

"But keeping the rules isn't enough" Jesus said out loud. "You've got to learn to be really generous too. You've got to share everything you have with people who are not as lucky as you are, and you mustn't keep anything just for yourself, and say 'that's my favourite thing, I'm not going to share that!' "

When the young man heard that he didn't look quite so pleased with himself. You see his Daddy was very rich, and the young man had lots and lots of 'favourite things', that he didn't want to share with anyone.

"If you really want to be sure that you will go to heaven" Jesus said (and you will remember that was the question the young man had asked Him in the first place) "You must sell everything you have got, and give the money away to the poor people. You will find that you can still be happy even if you haven't got lots of 'things'. And when you've done that, come back to Me and you can be one of My special friends, who travel about with Me so that they can learn all about God and the way He wants them to live."

When the young man heard that, he pulled a very sad face. (You can see him in the picture.)

He wanted to be sure of going to heaven but oh dear me! he certainly didn't want to give all his money away! That was asking too much!

He knew that he had got to choose. He had got to give all his favourite things away, and be a special friend of Jesus, and be sure that he would one day go to Heaven. Or he had to keep all his money and favourite things for himself and go right away from Jesus and forget all about Him.

At last he made up his mind. Very sadly he turned away from Jesus and started on his way home.

Jesus watched him go; He was very sad too.

"It's very hard for people who have lots of money and 'favourite things' to give them up and be My friend" He said. "In fact it is easier for a great big camel to squeeze through the eye of a needle than for a rich man to get into Heaven."

Jesus wasn't talking about sewing needles but about a little gate called a 'needle' that was set in the city wall. (You can see how hard it was for camels to get through in the picture.)

I hope that the next time your friends come to tea you will let them play with your special toy. I am sure they will be very, very careful.

A Prayer:
Dear Lord Jesus, Please help me to share the nice toys and books that I have and to give some of them away to children who are not as lucky as I am ; and help me not to be selfish, especially about the toy I like best. Amen.

45

9 The temple that was used as a market

I wonder if you sometimes use your bed for a trampoline and jump up and down on it? Or perhaps you take all the cushions off the settee and build a house with them? Does Mummy get cross? Does she say "I won't have your bed or my cushions used for the wrong purpose! A bed is meant for sleeping, not for jumping, and my cushions are for sitting on, not for building houses!" (You can see the children in the picture using the bed and the cushions for the wrong purposes.)

Jesus once got cross like that. He was cross with some people who were using the Temple—which is meant to be God's House—for the wrong purpose! I'll tell you about it.

Long ago people believed that if they wanted God to be pleased with them they must bring Him a present when they came to Church. They usually brought an animal or bird for the present. Sometimes it was a little lamb, and sometimes a calf, and sometimes a pair of white doves. They used to buy the animals or birds from a farmer in the village where they lived and bring them up to the big Temple Church in Jerusalem, when they came to the service there.

One day some of the shopkeepers in Jerusalem had an idea.

"We could make a lot of money if we opened a kind of market in Jerusalem" they said, "Then people could buy their animals and birds straight from us instead of bringing them all the way from their home villages."

"What a good idea!" another man agreed. "If we had the market just inside the Temple courtyard, the people could buy the animals and birds on their way to the service. It would be very handy for them, and we should make a lot of money." So they went and asked the Ministers in the big Temple Church for permission. Perhaps they promised to give some of the money they would earn to the Temple collections, because the Ministers said "Yes" straight away, and the shopkeepers had a very busy time setting up their stalls and putting the animals in pens and making sure they had plenty of change.

Soon it was time to open and the shopkeepers were kept very, very busy. People found it was useful to buy their presents for God on their way into the Temple, and the shopkeepers made lots and lots of money.

One day Jesus came to the Temple Church. (You can see Him in the archway.) He was very angry when He saw what was happening. You know how noisy a Saturday market can be? Well, it was just as noisy as that inside the Temple Church. The sheep were baa-ing—Baaaaaa. The calves were crying for their mothers

—Moooooo. The shopkeepers were shouting . . . "Come and buy my animals. They're the best in the market!" The doves were coo-ing. Cooooooo, Cooooooo. The money was chinking into the shopkeepers bowls—rattle-rattle chink-chink-chink. And if you and Mummy and Daddy and your brothers or sisters make all those noises loudly—at the top of your voices—all at once!—you will have some idea of how noisy it was!

Jesus grabbed a piece of rope, and He opened the pens and drove all the animals out of the Temple Church—just like you see a farmer driving his sheep or cows along a country road.

He turned upside down the bowls of money and said, "Take all this away!"

He knocked over the market stalls and said, "You're NOT to use God's House as a shop!"

He opened the cages and flapped His arms at the doves so that they all flew away free and said "You're not to use the Temple Church for the wrong purpose! God's House is for praying and singing praises. People can't pray and sing when it's as noisy as this!"

Do you remember that God's House is for singing praises and do you try to be quiet when you go inside? I expect you will now that you have heard this story!

A Prayer:
Dear Father God, When we go into Church help us to remember that it is Your House. Help us to be quiet and thoughtful, and to listen carefully and sing the songs with all our might. Amen.

10 The boy who shared his lunch

A roll spread with butter and mashed up egg.
A packet of potato crisps. An apple. A triangle
of cheese wrapped up in silver paper, and a
chocolate biscuit.

Is that the kind of lunch that Mummy gives
you when you go out for a picnic? It's just enough
for one, and perhaps Mummy puts it in a grease-
proof bag so that you can keep it separate.
(You can see this kind of lunch in the picture.)

I'm going to tell you a story about a little boy
and a picnic. He didn't have the same kind of
picnic that you have. His lunch was five little
bread rolls and two small herring sort of fishes
that his Mummy had cooked until they were all

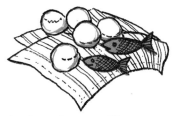

crunchy and crispy brown. (You can see them in the picture.) The boy was going out for the whole day to listen to Jesus who was very, very good at telling exciting and interesting stories.

The boy had to walk a long way before he found Jesus. There was a big crowd round Him (there must have been nearly five thousand people) and the boy had to squash himself in a very wriggly way before he could get near to the front. But he did it at last, and then he sat down on the grass to listen, and watch. Jesus didn't only tell stories, you will remember. He could also make sick people better, and it was very, very exciting seeing people hobble up all sad and limp and slow, and go away all happy and bouncy after they had been made well again.

When the sun had climbed up high in the sky Jesus remembered that it was lunch time. The boy remembered it was lunch time too, and he got out his picnic lunch and started to unwrap it. But nobody else seemed to have remembered to bring a picnic lunch, and the boy thought it would look greedy—eating all by himself. He sat there thinking, and looking round, and he didn't really know what to do.

While he was thinking and looking he heard Jesus speak to His friend Philip.

"How are we going to buy some bread so that all these people can have some lunch?" He said.

"We would need about fifteen pounds to buy enough bread for all this crowd" Philip replied, "And even then there would only be enough to give them a little bit each."

Then Andrew, another of Jesus' friends looked straight at the picnic boy and said to Jesus,

"There's a boy here who has five little rolls and a couple of fish, but what's the good of that for such a crowd."

Jesus smiled at the boy, and it was the kind of smile when your eyebrows go up a bit, so that you ask a question at the same time. Mummy or Daddy will show you the kind of smile I mean!

The boy knew that the smile really meant "Would you mind sharing your dinner with the rest of us?"

The boy was so pleased that Jesus had noticed him that he said "Yes" straight away, and scrambling to his feet he gave his picnic lunch into Jesus' hands. (Can you see him in the picture?)

And then something very wonderful happened. Jesus took the boy's picnic lunch and started to break the rolls and fish into little pieces and the special friends of Jesus started to hand it round, and they went on and on, until everybody in the crowd had had enough to eat! When everyone was full Jesus said to His friends, "Collect all the pieces that are left over so that nothing is wasted."

And when the men had done so, there were twelve baskets—full of left overs. (Can you count them in the picture?)

Everyone was very surprised. Jesus' friends were very surprised, but the picnic boy was the most surprised of all!

It was only a LITTLE lunch, but Jesus made it enough to feed five thousand people.

You may be only a LITTLE boy or girl, but Jesus can make you VERY useful if you only ask Him!

A Prayer:
Dear Lord Jesus. I know I am only little but I do want to be useful to You. Please take my hands and show me how I can help people with them. Please take my feet and let me run errands with them. Please take my lips and let me say kind things with them. Please take some of my pocket money and let me buy something for someone else. You used the little picnic boy. Please use me. Amen.

11 The widow who had nothing left

I wonder how much money you put into the collection plate at Church on Sundays, and where the money comes from? Perhaps Daddy gives you sixpence just before the collection hymn, or do you save a penny from your pocket money and get it out of your purse at the right time? Which of the children in the picture is being given money from Daddy, and which has saved it up?

Which do you think God is most pleased with—the money that Daddy gives you, or the money you have saved yourself? Perhaps this story will help you to find out the right answer.

One day, Jesus was sitting on a seat inside the Temple courtyard watching the people come in and out. Just beside Him was the big wooden chest where people put their collection money. It had a funnel leading down into the chest, rather like the funnel Daddy uses to fill the car up with petrol, or to put paraffin in the heater, but it was much bigger! When people put their money into the funnel, it made a loud rattling noise as it tumbled down into the chest, and the more money that people threw in, the more noise it made! (You can see the chest and the funnel in the picture.)

The rich people were rather pleased about the noise! It made people turn and stare when they put a whole handful of money in the box and the rich people thought to themselves—"I expect everyone is thinking how good I am to put so much money in the box when they hear my coins make such a lovely loud jangly sound."

Suddenly, through the Temple doorway came a little old woman. She was a widow. (A widow is a lady whose husband has died.) This widow had no way of earning any money and had no one to look after her, so she was very poor indeed. (Can you see her in the picture, with the old patched shawl around her head?)

The little old lady looked round in a rather frightened way. She didn't like coming into the big Temple Church where there were so many

rich and important people. Then, when she was sure that no one was looking, she tiptoed up to the big collection box and slid two mites down the big metal funnel. (A mite was the smallest coin there was.) So the tiny coins hardly made any noise at all—only a little tiny 'tink', 'tink' as they hit the bottom.

The widow thought that no one had seen her, but Someone had. It was Jesus. He knew that the widow woman was very, very poor—so poor that the two mites that she had put in the collection box were the very last coins that she had in her purse.

"Truly I say to you" Jesus said quietly to His friends, who were sitting with Him, "This poor widow has put in more than all those other people who are giving money to the Temple collection. For the rich people had plenty of money left, but this woman has given everything she had, and now she has nothing left for herself at all."

NOW do you know the answer to the question at the beginning of this story? When Daddy gives you money out of his pocket, it's a very EASY way of giving, isn't it? But it's much harder to give money out of your very own pocket money, especially if it's the last money you have left, and it will mean that you will have nothing left for sweets!

A Prayer:
Dear Lord Jesus, Help me to put aside some of my pocket money so that the pennies I give really come from me, because I know this is the kind of giving that You really like best. Amen.

12 The sick man who remembered to say thank you

Are you good at remembering to say 'thank you' or do you sometimes forget? Do you expect your friends to say 'thank you' if you give them a birthday present, or lend them your rubber at school? This is a story about nine people who forgot to say 'thank you' and the one person who remembered. (The sum in the picture will remind you what this story is about.)

```
Healed      10
Thank you    1
           ____
   forgot    9
```

Do you sometimes fall down and get a nasty sore graze on your knee? It looks horrid, doesn't it? And I expect you are very pleased when it all heals up again with nice new skin. The ten men in my story all had nasty sore places on their knees. They had nasty sore places on their arms too, and on their hands and their faces and their feet, which hurt a lot, and never seemed to

get better. They had a very bad illness called leprosy, and none of the doctors knew how to make them well again.

"We don't want anyone else to catch the illness" the doctors said, "You must go away from your homes and your families and live somewhere quite on your own." (It was rather like having chicken pox and not being able to have any friends to visit you.)

"Perhaps we shall get better soon," the men said, but they didn't! The illness got worse and worse until at last there were so many sore places that there was hardly any nice smooth skin at all.

The men were very unhappy and they were very lonely too. Sometimes people put bowls of food just outside the village and the sick men would come and collect it. (Can you see them in the picture?) But the village people would never come near them, in case they should catch the illness themselves.

One day, when the ten men had come down to the village for food they saw a great crowd of people coming along the street.

"I think it is Jesus" one of them said, "He is Someone Special and He does the most wonderful things. I have heard that He can make people who are ill quite well again."

"Why don't we ask Him to make us well again?" one of the men asked. And they all decided that would be a very good idea.

They hurried to meet Jesus. Everyone else ran away because they didn't want to catch leprosy.

For lepers — Keep away please

"Jesus" the men called, "Please take pity on us and make us better."

"Yes, I will" Jesus said. "I will make you quite well again. You must go and show yourself to the priest in the Temple." (A priest was a kind of minister.) "He has to be sure you are quite well before he will let you go back home again."

"We'll go this very minute!" the men said, and off they went.

Down the road they hurried towards the Temple, walking as fast as their legs would carry them and then suddenly they stopped.

They looked at their hands. They were quite healed. They looked at their arms. They were quite healed. They looked at their legs. They were quite healed. They looked at their feet. They were quite healed. They looked at each other's faces. They were quite healed.

"We're healed!" they shouted, "We're quite better! We'll go and show ourselves to the priest and then we can go back and live with our families again. Hurray! Hurray! Hurray!" and they hurried on again.

Suddenly, one of them stopped and started to come back. (You can see him in the picture.)

"I forgot!" he said to Jesus, "I forgot to say 'thank you'! I was so excited and pleased, I forgot to say thank you!"

"That's all right" Jesus said, "But I'm glad you remembered. But where are the other nine men? They didn't say thank you, either."

But the other nine men were just like little dots in the distance. (You can just see them in the picture.) They had forgotten all about saying thank you to Jesus, who had used His wonderful power to make them quite well again.

I'm glad the man remembered to say thank you in the end, aren't you? But I wish the other nine had remembered as well!

A Prayer:
Dear God, Please remind me of all the things that I should say 'thank you' for. For my Mummy and Daddy; my home; my school; my teacher and my friends; I want to say 'thank you' to You too, because You love me and care about me so much. Amen.